CONTENTS

KENNEDY SPACE CENTER, NASA

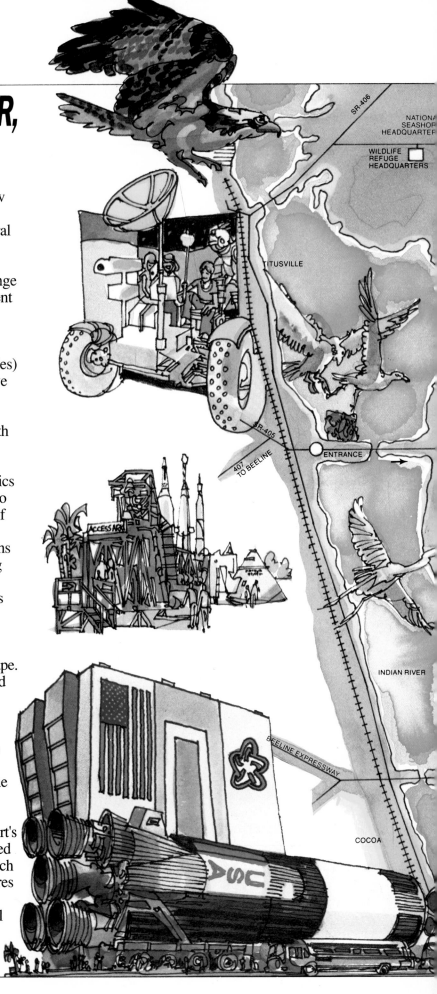

In the years following World War II, America's military rockets began to outgrow the range available in the western desert, so the War Department selected Cape Canaveral as the testing area for long-range guided missiles. Formal approval of the site was given on June 1949, and the Joint Long Range Proving Ground was designated by President Truman as the site for test-launching early U.S. Missiles. Cape Canaveral Air Force Station is Station One of a test range that extends over 16,000 kilometers (10,000 miles) into the Indian Ocean. During its most active period in the early 1960's, there were more than 20 working launch pads on the Cape. Later, in the 1960's, it became known as both the Eastern Test Range and the Atlantic Missile Range.

On October 1, 1958, the National Aeronautics and Space Administration was established to carry out the peaceful exploration and use of space.

The early focus of NASA's launch operations centered on Cape Canaveral, where existing rockets and launch pads were modified and used to launch early satellites and astronauts of the Mercury and Gemini programs. Communications and science satellites and automated spacecraft to explore our Solar System are still being launched from the Cape. In late 1962, initial preparations commenced for the construction of NASA's Launch Complex 39 to handle the Apollo-Saturn V launch vehicles and later modified to accommodate the launch and landing of the Space Shuttle. These reusable spaceplanes have made repeated trips into space since the first of the fleet, Columbia, made its flight debut in 1981.

All but the operational areas of the Spaceport's 34,000 hectares (84,000 acres) are designated as a National Wildlife Refuge, much of which is open to the public. In 1975, 16,600 hectares (41,000 acres) of the Spaceport were designated as part of the Canaveral National Seashore.

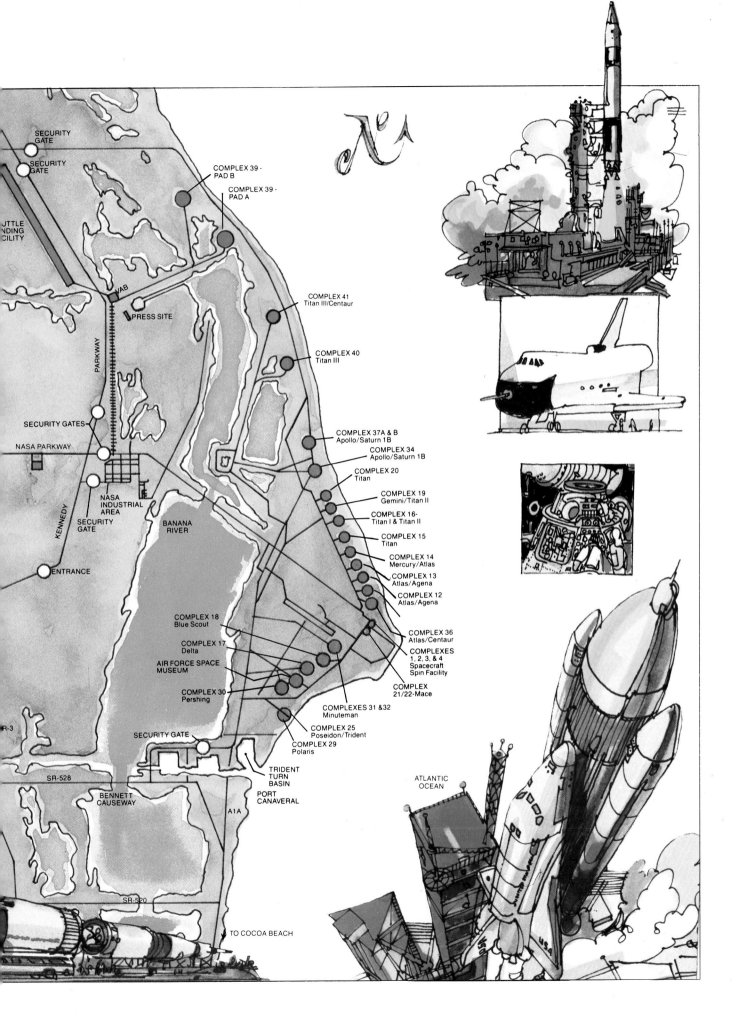

SECURITY GATE

SECURITY GATE

SHUTTLE LANDING FACILITY

COMPLEX 39 - PAD B

COMPLEX 39 - PAD A

VAB

PRESS SITE

PARKWAY

COMPLEX 41
Titan III/Centaur

COMPLEX 40
Titan III

SECURITY GATES

NASA PARKWAY

KENNEDY

NASA INDUSTRIAL AREA

SECURITY GATE

COMPLEX 37A & B
Apollo/Saturn 1B

COMPLEX 34
Apollo/Saturn 1B

COMPLEX 20
Titan

COMPLEX 19
Gemini/Titan II

COMPLEX 16-
Titan I & Titan II

COMPLEX 15
Titan

COMPLEX 14
Mercury/Atlas

COMPLEX 13
Atlas/Agena

COMPLEX 12
Atlas/Agena

ENTRANCE

BANANA RIVER

COMPLEX 18
Blue Scout

COMPLEX 17
Delta

AIR FORCE SPACE MUSEUM

COMPLEX 30
Pershing

COMPLEX 36
Atlas/Centaur

COMPLEXES
1, 2, 3, & 4
Spacecraft
Spin Facility

COMPLEX
21/22-Mace

COMPLEXES 31 & 32
Minuteman

SR-3

COMPLEX 25
Poseidon/Trident

COMPLEX 29
Polaris

SECURITY GATE

TRIDENT TURN BASIN

PORT CANAVERAL

ATLANTIC OCEAN

SR-528

BENNETT CAUSEWAY

A1A

SR-520

TO COCOA BEACH

TOUR INFORMATION

Guided bus tours of the Kennedy Space Center are offered every day of the year except Christmas Day. They offer enlightening glimpses into the accomplishments of the past and the challenges and opportunities that await us in the future. Your tour covers terrain first viewed by the exploring Spaniards four and half centuries ago and the training grounds and launch facilities for astronauts who walked upon the surface of the Moon. Along the tour route, WHICH MAY BE VARIED SLIGHTLY DUE TO OPERATIONAL REQUIREMENTS, you will view the Industrial Area with its administrative offices, laboratories and processing facilities for Space Shuttle payloads. A tour stop at the Flight Crew Training Building includes a dramatic sight and sound show with a real Lunar Module on a realistic simulation of the Moon's surface.

Your tour will take you to the massive facilities of Complex 39, launch site for the daring Apollo voyages to the Moon, and Skylab, America's first space station. Complex 39 is now the home of the Space Shuttle. Here you may stop adjacent to the Vehicle Assembly Building (VAB) one of the world's largest structures, and the Apollo/Saturn V, that carried man to the Moon. You will view the giant crawler-transporters which move Mobile Launch Platforms and flight hardware from the VAB to the launch pads. OPERATIONS PERMITTING you will view launch pads at Complex 39 where Apollo/Saturn rockets rumbled into space on tongues of flame and from where the Space Shuttle is launched. You will view the Press Site from which space missions are covered by news media representatives from around the world.

When the Space Shuttle is on the launch pad, restrictions on tour routes due to safety and security requirements may prevent stops for picture taking and require that bus windows not be opened.

Spaceport USA entrance.

You will be leaving the bus at several points of interest. Each time you leave the bus, please take all of your possessions with you, since it is possible that you may not return to the same bus. As you get off the bus or as you approach stairways or parking curbs, please step carefully. While off the bus, please stay together as a group and do not leave the area near the bus. And, most important, please keep your conversation to a minimum so that everyone can hear your tour escort. Thank you for your cooperation.

We here at the Kennedy Space Center are ready to serve you in every way we possibly can. We want your visit to be a thrilling and informative experience you will long remember.

We would like to remind you that if you have a pet, please do not leave the pet in your automobile. We have free kennel service. If you want your pet to have food or water, please provide the food or water and the serving dishes. Check in at the Departure Control office for details.

Our bilingual Information Agents may be able to help in currency exchange, provide information on how to get to the next stop on your tour of the Sunshine State and, of course, help you understand any American words or phrases that are difficult to translate.

A Space Coast Area Information booth is located in Spaceport Central for information on local accommodations and restaurants.

Entrance to Kennedy Space Center.

Bus tour and IMAX Theater tickets are sold at the outdoor Ticket Pavilion.

Tour America's Spaceport in air conditioned comfort.

Visitors to the Kennedy Space Center often have a chance to see a Space Shuttle on a launch pad being readied for a flight.

■ SPACEPORT USA

An aerial view of Spaceport USA–a look into our space programs past, present and future!

Monument – "In Memory of those who in the line of duty have given their lives to Space Exploration."

History and the future are combined in this mural depicting United States manned space exploration.

Suit up for your photo album.

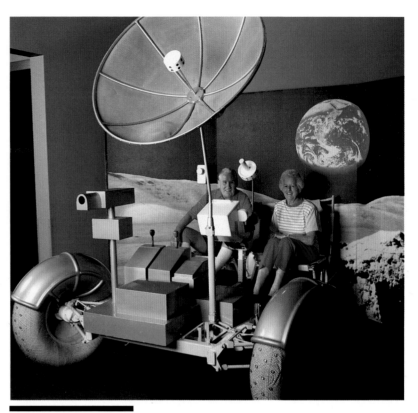

Sit on a Lunar Rover–Imagine being on the Moon.

In the "Satellites and You" exhibit, learn how satellites in space have down to Earth applications.

GALAXY CENTER

The Galaxy Center, located at the north end of Spaceport USA, provides visitors with a variety of enjoyable attractions. The IMAX and Galaxy Theaters, space art, and informative space exhibits are housed inside the Galaxy Center.

Galaxy Center has a futuristic look.

Visitors enjoy space art.

Full size model of the flight deck of a Space Shuttle Orbiter.

Visitors get a good perspective of the size and scope of a fully assembled Space Shuttle as they view this scale model.

Model of the Hubble Space Telescope, deployed from the Space Shuttle Orbiter in 1990.

In the IMAX Theater watch the astronauts work in space on a 5 1/2 story high screen.

The Galaxy Theater is a place to relax and enjoy a presentation on our future in space.

GALLERY OF SPACEFLIGHT

Spaceport USA visitors relive the past achievements of manned space explorations as they view spacecraft and space suits of the early manned space missions.

The Gallery of Spaceflight has on display a combination of actual space hardware and models which portray many of the significant programs and events that have occurred in space exploration. A self-guiding path takes visitors through historic events spanning both manned and unmanned efforts to conquer, understand and utilize the unique and sometimes mysterious place called Outer Space.

Both these spacecraft have been in orbit. At left is Gemini 9, flown by two astronauts in 1966. On the right is the actual Apollo spacecraft that carried three American astronauts to a space linkup with two Soviet cosmonauts in 1975.

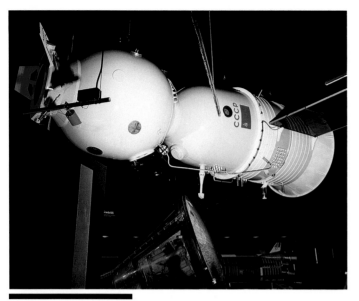

Full size model of the Russian Soyuz spacecraft which docked with an Apollo spacecraft in 1975.

Gemini Space Suit worn by Astronaut David Scott on the Gemini 8 mission in March 1966.

This one-tenth scale model of the Saturn V Moon Rocket and Apollo spacecraft is cut away to show the inner workings of this famous space vehicle.

GALLERY OF SPACEFLIGHT

A lunar rock collected by Moon-walking Apollo astronauts is on display.

A collection of colorful mission emblems used in the Apollo Lunar Landing Program. Each emblem tells a story of its own.

Full size model of a Lunar Rover.

Just like walking through space.

Full size detailed model of the Viking Mars Lander. In 1976 two spacecraft landed on Mars, the Red Planet, to gather important information about the surface and the atmosphere.

ROCKET GARDEN

Many of the rockets used for both manned and unmanned spaceflight are displayed in an area of Spaceport USA known as the Rocket Garden.

A full scale model of the lunar module that astronauts used to land on the moon.

Access Arm once used by Apollo 11 crew, astronauts Armstrong, Aldrin, and Collins.

Actual Saturn 1B Rocket like those used in the first manned Apollo launch and the three visits to the Skylab orbiting station.

GIFT GANTRY, ORBIT CAFETERIA & LUNCH PAD

Be sure to visit Spaceport USA's Gift Gantry.

You will find many remembrances of U.S. spaceflights and ample "necessities" for young astronauts. An exciting array of gift items ranging from model rockets to astronaut flight suits are available as are pictures of spaceflights, rockets, astronauts, the earth, the moon, and slide series that depict specific missions of NASA. Souvenir pencils, pens, banners and coins are also available. If you like to put models together this is an ideal place for model builders.

A variety of food services are available for hungry visitors. The selection of tasty items ranges from chicken dinners to ice cream cones. An unusual feature in the Orbit Cafeteria is a "wheel" that brings the food to the customer.

■ KENNEDY SPACE CENTER

This is where your tour begins . . . At this nation's major launch base for all manned and most unmanned spacecraft. America's Spaceport is operated by NASA– the National Aeronautics and Space Administration (a civilian agency of the government.)

On the tour you will be able to see some of the launch facilities used in NASA's exploration of outer space.

This is where the efforts of thousands of people from all walks of life have been brought together to achieve this nation's goals in space exploration. Space activity, over the years, has generated worldwide interest. We hope that after you have seen our facilities and have heard our story you will have a much better understanding of what we are really trying to do in space–that is, to benefit mankind, on Earth.

Start your tour in air conditioned comfort.

The Central Instrumentation Facility is filled with space-age computers. All pre-flight and launch data of NASA's unmanned space vehicles is fed from launch pads to these computers. The computers provide printed, tape-recorded or televised data for use in analyzing rocket and spacecraft performance. Laboratories and workshops where some 24,000 pieces of delicate test equipment are calibrated or repaired in support of launch activities are also in this building.

The Communications Distribution and Switching Center, a vital part of Space Center operations, uses a huge dish-shaped radio antenna as a satellite communications link between the Kennedy Space Center, Mission Control in Houston, Texas, NASA Headquarters in Washington, D.C. and other NASA Centers. The antenna dish, constructed entirely of aluminum, is 11 meters (35 feet) in diameter, and parabolic in shape. The relay satellite is essentially stationary in orbit, the antenna is also fixed in place and doesn't require a complicated tracking system.

The Headquarters Building is where the management offices are located for all operations underway at the Kennedy Space Center.

The Headquarters Building is the administrative center for all Spaceport activities. The director of the Kennedy Space Center and his deputy plus many of the management staff and several hundred contractor and support personnel work in the offices located throughout this large structure. This government-industry team consists of 2,300 federal workers and 16,000 employees representing a large number of American and international industrial firms.

Operations and Checkout Building.

The Operations and Checkout Building is the largest structure in the industrial area. Here, spacecraft used for the Moon landing missions, as well as Skylab and the joint mission with the Soviet Union in 1975 were prepared for launch. In this same building Spacelab, which is the European Space Agency's contribution to the Space Shuttle program, is checked out prior to being fitted into the cargo bay of the Shuttle Orbiter. The building's tallest section is the highbay, where Spacelab and other Space Shuttle payloads are assembled and checked out.
When astronaut crews are assigned here for an upcoming mission, they occupy living quarters on the third floor.

Flight Crew Training Building.

The Flight Crew Training Building was the focal point in the training of Apollo astronaut crews for their flights to the Moon and return to Earth. Inside the building were very complex and large machines called simulators which enabled the astronauts to rehearse every detail of their flights to and from the Moon. The most knowledgeable engineers trained the astronauts, who communicated with their flight controllers in Houston, Texas as they would during an actual flight. Not just hours, but months of training went into every

moment of a flight. Scale models, movies and video tapes all helped to provide realistic training. When the astronauts emerged from their training they were ready for real flight.

Today, this facility is primarily occupied by engineers and technicians who work on the sophisticated Launch Processing System used to check out and launch our current spaceship, the Space Shuttle.

Apollo launch control firing room is recreated in the Flight Crew Training Building.

Manned lunar landing missions in the Apollo program were accomplished using two independently operating spacecraft which flew from Earth to the Moon docked together. The Command Module served as home for the three crew members during their roundtrip. The Lunar Module served as home during the time spent on the lunar surface.

Each spacecraft had its own life support system and rocket engines to power their movement. In all, there were nine missions to the moon, including six Lunar landings. Each flight consisted of three crewmen, who would spend most of a typical lunar mission in the Command Module. Only during the landing portion of a flight would two crewmen enter the Lunar Module for exploration of the lunar surface.

Apollo Command Module with door in open position.

A real Apollo Lunar Module is displayed for tour visitors on a simulated landing site.

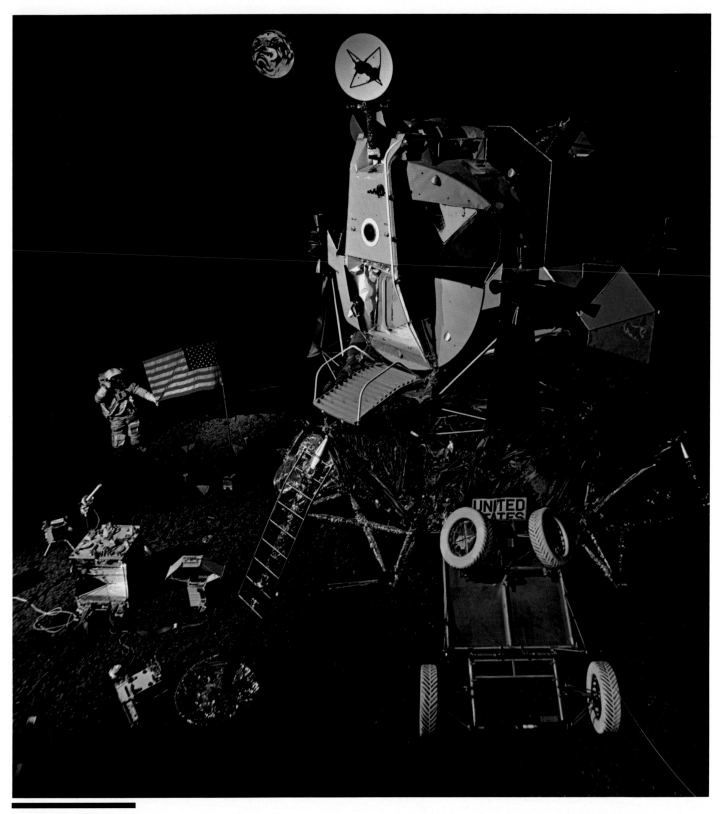

Simulated Lunar Landing Site.

This is a real Lunar Module. You can see the hatchway from which the two space explorers emerged to step on the surface of the Moon. The Lunar Rover is carried in the lower section of the Lunar Module. Once on the surface and ready to go, it could travel a total of nearly 64 kilometers (40 miles) at speeds up to 16 kph (10 mph).

The Vehicle Assembly Building and the Shuttle Landing Facility where the Orbiter could land after a mission in space.

The Vehicle Assembly Building is one of the world's largest structures in volume, enclosing about 3,664,833 cubic meters (129,428,000 cubic feet).

It is here that Space Shuttles are asembled into flight-ready space vehicles before being taken to the launch pad.

Once an Orbiter is moved from the Orbiter Processing Facility into the Vehicle Assembly Building, huge cranes lift it to the top of the building, then slowly across the center aisle into the selected bay where the Mobile Launcher awaits. Cranes earlier carried the two solid fuel rocket boosters, the external fuel tank and other flight components to the Mobile Launcher, where engineers and technicians assembled them during a lengthy, painstaking process. The Orbiter is the last major component to be joined to the stack. Many more checks are made before the Crawler Transporter moves the tremendous load out to the launch site, a trip that takes about seven hours at maximum speed of 1.6 kilometers per hour (1 mph).

The Shuttle Landing Facility, seen in the upper left of the picture, is 4,572 meters (15,000 feet) long and 91.4 meters (300 feet) wide. It has 305 meters (1,000 feet) of paved overruns at each end. The paving thickness is 40.6 cm (16 inches). The landing strip includes a 150 x 168 meter (490 x 550 foot) parking apron and a 3.2 km (2 mile) tow-way road connecting it with the Orbiter Processing Facility where the Orbiter is prepared before being taken into the Vehicle Assembly Building.

THE ORBITER PROCESSING FACILITY

The Orbiter Processing Facility (OPF) is used for servicing the Space Shuttle Orbiter and can be compared to a hangar where aircraft are repaired, overhauled or serviced for flight. The OPF has two service areas where engine servicing or replacement, thermal protection system check out, and even cargo loading or unloading can be done. After each mission, highly trained crews review every orbiter system to ensure the rigors of flight have not compromised the Orbiter's ability to perform the hundreds of tasks required for a successful space mission. The OPF is uniquely outfitted to efficiently accomplish its assignments.

Shuttle Orbiter on its way to the Vehicle Assembly Building.

Space Shuttle Columbia moves out of the Orbiter Processing Facility.

Night view of runway at KSC.

The most modern landing system ever devised is used to guide the Orbiter to its touchdown point on this runway.

Automatic guidance is initiated at a point where the Orbiter has a very sharp angle of entry, over seven times that of a commercial aircraft approach. The descent rate is greater than 3,048 meters (10,000 feet) per minute–approximately 20 times that of a commercial airliner.

The Orbiter can be guided and landed automatically by onboard computers. If there is any variation, the crew can take over at any time for a manually controlled landing.

Inside the Mate-Demate Device, the Orbiter Columbia is off-loaded from NASA's 747 Shuttle Carrier aircraft. Demate crews work through the night uncoupling the Orbiter from its carrier.

The Saturn V rocket on display outside the Vehicle Assembly Building is separated at its staging points to allow visitors a good view of the engines for each stage. Standing vertically, the rocket and spacecraft, tower at 111 meters (363 feet) and weigh 2,812 metric tons (6.2 million pounds). The Saturn V carried the Apollo missions to the Moon and is the world's most powerful launch vehicle.

This is an awe inspiring view of the five first stage rocket engines of the Saturn V. Each of these engines produces 1.5 million pounds of thrust—a total of 7.5 million pounds at lift off. These powerful engines propelled the astronauts on the first leg of their journey to the Moon.

The crawler transporter backs away from the mobile launch platform and the shuttle stack at Pad 39A.

THE CRAWLER TRANSPORTER

The two Crawler Transporters at the Kennedy Space Center are very special machines designed to move space vehicles to the launch pad. A transporter can lift and carry 6,577,200 kg (14,500,000 pounds).

Each transporter is about half the size of a soccer field and weighs over 2,722 metric tons (6 million pounds). Propulsion is provided by two powerful diesel electric generators. The generators, in turn, power electric motors which turn the treads.

Normal speed of the transporter is 1.6 kilometers per hour (1 mph) when it has a load on top, but without a load it moves along rather quickly - 3.2 kilometers per hour (2 mph).

A hydraulic system can vary the transporter's height at either or both ends by as much as two meters (6 feet); thus, the transporter's cargo can be kept level at all times. The transporter requires a crew of 26. The driver sits in a glass-enclosed cab facing the direction of travel.

Each cleat weighs 907 kilograms (one ton). Each of the eight tracks on the Transporter has 57 cleats or a total of 456 cleats for a grand total of 413,592 kilograms (approx. 912,000 lbs.) of solid steel. The pins which connect the tracks weigh about 45.4 kilograms (100 lbs.) each.

In 1977 the American Society of Mechanical Engineers designated the Transporters of Launch Complex 39 as a "National Historic Mechanical Engineering Landmark."

A technician walks beside the treads of the giant crawler transporter as it creeps down the crawlerway.

Crawler Transporter

Space Shuttle being rolled out to the launch pad.

Inside the tallest section of the Vehicle Assembly Building are four equally sized high bays. It is in these high bays that the different elements of the Space Shuttle are assembled and readied for flight. The shorter portion of the facility contains four low bays. Checkout and refurbishment of various sections of solid rocket boosters are done in this part of the Vehicle Assembly Building. The dwarfed, four-story structure adjacent to the Vehicle Assembly Building is the Launch Control Center. There are three firing rooms in the Launch Control Center. It is here that pre-launch testing of the Space Shuttle is controlled and monitored and where the command to "go for launch" is issued.

When the Shuttle is on the launch pad, it is sometimes possible for our visitors to see and photograph the vehicle as it waits to be launched.
NASA and the aerospace industry have developed this revolutionary new transportation system for routine operations in space. With its versatility and reusability, the Space Shuttle opens the door to space.

Shuttle operations have encouraged many nations as well as private industry to participate in a variety of space ventures. Joint experiments and enterprises will help make the benefits of space exploration and technology more widely available to millions of people around the world.

Europe is already a major partner in the Shuttle. Ten nations of the European Space Agency have designed, funded and built "Spacelab" which is a versatile and reusable flight unit carried in the huge cargo bay of the Orbiter. Austria, Belgium, Denmark, France, Germany, Italy, Holland, Spain, Switzerland and the United Kingdom all share in the operations of Spacelab, with the United States. Canada provided the 15.2 meter (50 foot) remote manipulator arm which deploys and retrieves payloads in space.

The Shuttle Era began just over 20 years after the first American satellite in space, the "Explorer I" in 1958.

This historic area has been transformed into the place from where the Space Shuttle ventures into Earth orbit, enabling us to capitalize on knowledge gained from all previous space programs.

The crawlerway is a specially constructed roadway designed to support the tremendous loads of transporter and Shuttle while it travels from the Vehicle Assembly Building to the launch pad. The river rock surface covers a layer of asphalt and two meter (7 foot) bed of crushed stone. The distance from the VAB to the pad is 5.6 kilometers (3.5 miles).

THE LAUNCH PAD

The launch pad is constructed of 52,000 cubic meters (68,000 cubic yards) of reinforced concrete. On top of the pad are six steel pedestals used to support the launch platform and the shuttle package. Nearby are two service towers. The tallest one is in a fixed position, and the shorter one is mounted on wheels so that it can swing away from the shuttle. These towers provide access to the rocket for astronaut boarding, payload installation, fueling and final checkout before launch.

During the actual launch, water spouts located in the flame trench and on the mobile launch platform will dump over 1.1 million liters (300,000 gallons) of water onto the pad area during a 20-second period to provide sound suppression and cooling.

Space Shuttle arrives at Pad 39A after a 3-1/2 mile journey from the Vehicle Assembly Building.

The hazy light of dawn illuminates the Space Shuttle Columbia as it sits on Pad 39A.

■ BEHIND THE SCENES

In this decade men and women of many nations have gone into space to conduct important scientific and technical experiments using the capability provided by Spacelab.

Spacelab development is financed by ten European nations under agreements with the European Space Agency.

Spacelab is a modular structure carried in the cargo bay of the Orbiter to meet varying mission requirements. The two main components are the pressurized module, which provides a laboratory with a shirt-sleeve working environment and the open pallet, that exposes materials and equipment directly to space. Upon return to Earth, the module or pallet is removed, refurbished and readied for another flight.

Orbiter refurbishment, including cleaning, heat shield servicing, component testing and parts replacement are accomplished in the Orbiter Processing Facility (OPF). Each time an Orbiter returns from a mission, it is returned to the OPF for a complete check up and then readied for the next mission. Also, any horizontal payloads such as the Spacelab are loaded into the Orbiter's Cargo Bay while still in the OPF.

In the Operations and Checkout Building places of the European built Spacelab are assembled, tested and readied for launch.

Space Shuttle Orbiters are serviced and readied for flight in the Orbiter Processing Facility (OPF).

Astronauts Joe Engle and Richard Truly inspect the Remote Manipulator System (RMS) in the Orbiter Processing Facility, as it undergoes preparation and installation in the cargo bay of the Columbia. The RMS, built in Canada, is designed to move orbital hardware from the cargo bay into space and, help retrieve disabled satellites and other space hardware from low Earth orbit.

The Orbiter's cargo hold, with payload attachment points along its full length, is adaptable enough to accommodate as many as five unmanned spacecraft of various sizes and shapes on a single mission. Payloads include instruments that view Earth or outer space, small self-contained experiments for a variety of users, satellites, or a fully equipped manned scientific laboratory. The Orbiter supplies payloads with electrical power, heating and cooling, data transmission or storage, displays for the payload specialists aboard, and communications with ground stations. For instruments that make their observations from platforms in the payload bay, the Orbiter's computers fire the small attitude-control thrusters to maintain pointing accuracy within half of a degree.

OSTA-1, first Space Shuttle payload, with experiments for remote sensing of land resources, environmental quality, ocean conditions and meteorological phenomena.

Space Shuttle launches are conducted by personnel manning these consoles in Firing Room 1, and from similar consoles in NASA's other two Firing Rooms. The launch Control Center is equipped with the highly automated Launch Processing System, designed for Space Shuttle checkout and launch.

Solid rocket booster segments arriving at KSC are transported into High Bay 4 in the Vehicle Assembly Building and mated to their aft skirts. The two aft assemblies support the entire 45 meter (150 foot) tall boosters, in turn supporting the external tank and Orbiter on the mobile launcher platform.

Assembly of the first Space Shuttle was completed on November 26, 1980 with the mating of the Orbiter Columbia to its external tank in the Vehicle Assembly Building. Space Shuttle Discovery, shown at lower right attached to its hoisting sling, was moved into the VAB after having completed tests and tile installation in the adjacent Orbiter Processing Facility. The other Shuttle components, the twin solid rocket boosters and the external propellant tank, were stacked on the mobile launcher platform earlier.

"Stacking" the solid rocket booster segments in the Vehicle Assembly Building.

An engineer is lowered into the core of the solid rocket booster for inspection.

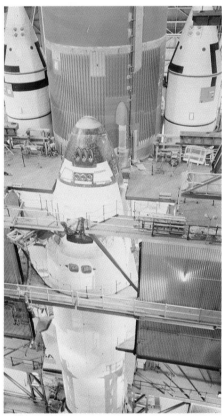

Discovery being mated to the twin solid rocket booster and the external fuel tank in the Vehicle Assembly Building.

Workers install thermal protection.

Space Shuttle Orbiter being prepared to be lifted up and mated to already prepared fuel tank and rocket boosters.

Insulation tough enough to protect the Orbiter and its crew from the searing heat of repeated re-entries had to be invented. In earlier manned spacecraft, thermal buildup was controlled by shedding glowing bits of the heat shield itself. But, for the Shuttle, NASA needed materials that would last through 100 missions before replacement. The answer was a special tile-like insulation that reflects heat so effectively that when one side is cool enough to hold in your bare hands, the other side can be red hot.

Following its move from the Orbiter Processing Facility to the giant Vehicle Assembly Building, the Space Shuttle Orbiter Columbia is prepared for hoisting and mating operations with the external tank, which will complete the assembly of the first Space Shuttle vehicle. Attached to its handling sling, the Orbiter will be rotated to a vertical position, lifted 59.5 meters (190 feet) above the VAB floor, then swung over a large structural beam and slowly lowered to the deck of a mobile launcher platform in the assembly bay for mating with its external tank.

Personnel practice emergency water rescue operations using manikins to simulate an astronaut crew member. The maneuvers were first conducted on a wood and fiberglass mock-up of the Orbiter at a small pond south of the Shuttle Landing Facility in the summer of 1980.

During recovery operations, each ship will pick up one of the boosters, its three parachutes, and nose cone.

One of two specially outfitted ships used to recover the boosters from the sea after each launch of the Space Shuttle.

Specially designed parachutes are used to slow the jettisoned rocket booster casings to a soft landing in the Atlantic Ocean.

The highly trained recovery crew uses special equipment to handle the solid rocket boosters.

Aerial view of solid rocket booster disassembly and refurbishment facility.

■ SHUTTLE ERA

The Space Shuttle is America's most versatile manned spacecraft ever. It's maiden flight in 1981 marked the real beginning of space travel. For, unlike its predecessors Mercury, Gemini and Apollo - the Shuttle is a reusable spaceship, designed for years of service and capable of making repeated roundtrips to orbit.

The Shuttle provides flexibility never before achieved in space operations, and allows space to be routinely used as the resource it is.

The Orbiter's large cargo capacity and relatively mild launch environment enable it to carry into orbit a variety of satellites, including some which could not be launched before because of size, shape, weight or sensitivity to launch forces. Shuttle astronauts have delivered into orbit satellites for communications, Earth observations, scientific research and military purposes. They have recovered and repaired disabled spacecraft and they have dispatched robot probes to the planets. They have conducted medical and other tests to help identify problems and possibilities that might face future space travelers on long-term flights aboard a space station or on trips to Mars.

Soon, Shuttles will be used to ferry into low Earth orbit, sections of Space Station Freedom and the astronauts that will assemble them to build an outpost and laboratory in space

The potential of space is unlimited. The United States has been able to and will continue to utilize space for the benefit of mankind.

The Space Shuttle was developed by NASA, the National Aeronautics and Space Administration.

NASA manages and operates the Space Shuttle, including coordination of launch and space flight requirements for civil, government, commercial and military use.

The Space Shuttle system consists of three primary elements: an Orbiter spacecraft with three powerful liquid-fueled main engines, two solid-fueled booster rockets and an External Tank to hold fuel (liquid hydrogen) and oxidizer (liquid oxygen).

Shaped like an airplane, the 37.2 meter (122 foot) long Orbiter lifts off like a rocket, orbits like a spacecraft and returns to Earth on a landing strip like a glider or an airplane. It can transport and place in Earth orbit cargos weighing up to 29,484 kilograms (65,000 pounds). This cargo is carried in a bay 5 meters (15 feet) in diameter and 18 meters (60 feet) long. It can bring back from space cargo weighing as much as 14,515 kilograms (32,000 pounds).

The forward fuselage structure of the Orbiter is composed of aluminum alloy panels, frames and bulkheads. The crew cabin is supported within the fuselage by four attach points and is welded to create a pressure-tight vessel. The crew module has a side hatch for normal entry and exit and a hatch from the airlock into the payload bay for space walk access to the outside.

When the Shuttle era began with the launch of Columbia on April 12, 1981, astronauts John Young and Robert Crippen piloted the revolutionary new spaceship on a relatively-brief 54-hour test flight that took them 36 times around the world. Commander Young called it a "dream machine" and the flight duration and size of the crew gradually were increased for later flights.

FLIGHT CREW

The space agency for several years drew its astronaut candidates from the ranks of military test pilots. But by the mid-1960's, officials began to enlist scientists and engineers, and many with no flight experience, into the astronaut corps. The first scientist-astronaut, Harrison Schmitt, landed on the moon during the 1972 Apollo 17 mission, and put his expertise as a geologist to work in identifying and collecting lunar rocks.

When NASA began recruiting of astronauts for the Space Shuttle missions in the 1970's there were many qualified women applicants and in 1983, Sally Ride became the first American woman to rocket into space, aboard the seventh Space Shuttle mission. Other women have followed, contributing much to the space research and development projects during numerous trips into Earth orbit. The Space Shuttle era allowed NASA to fly doctors, engineers, astronomers and scientists who were not career astronauts, but were expert in their fields.

NASA recruits a new class of 15 to 20 astronauts every year or two. These candidates join the corps after they have received a one-year training course at the Johnson Space Center in Houston, Texas. Often they wait several years before they are assigned a flight, for which they train for about a year. There are four categories of assignments on shuttle missions: commander, pilot, mission specialist and payload specialist. Each crew consists of five to seven members who are selected based on the flight assignment and skills needed and their ability to get along with one another.

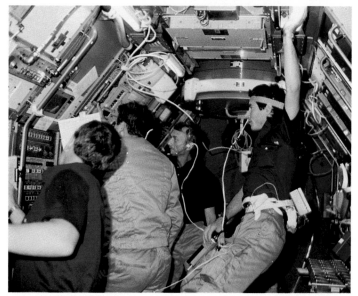

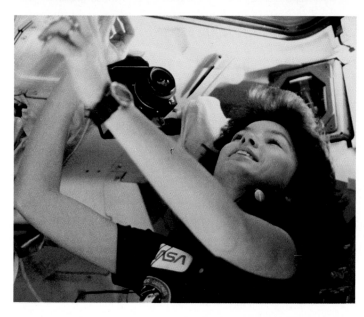

Once in orbit, Space Shuttle astronauts busy themselves in their weightless world with routine maintenance (top), science and technology experiments in a Spacelab module fitted into the cargo bay (center) and photographing the Earth or space phenomena (bottom). (opposite) Astronaut William F. Fisher works on a satellite.

■ SATELLITES

When the first American satellite rocketed into orbit on Jan. 31,1958, it carried a simple geiger counter to measure space radiation. It discovered a vast radiation belt surrounding the Earth and extending from about 400 to 40,000 miles out into space. The discovery stunned the scientific world, which generally believed the Earth's upper air merged into the density of interplanetary gas at an altitude of about 600 miles. The findings also created a revolution in the space sciences by demonstrating the ability of satellites to gather information from above the distorting influence of the dense lower level of the atmosphere. Scientists at NASA and in universities and research laboratories began devising ever-more-sophisticated instruments to probe not only Earth space, but the moon, stars and planets.

From this research there evolved satellites that have revolutionized global communications, maritime navigation, worldwide weather forecasting, military reconnaissance, search and rescue operations, and our knowledge of the Earth and its resources. From the frozen wastelands of the far north to remote jungle islands, the world has been drawn closer together by communications satellites. Telephones and television sets have sprouted where they never had been seen before. Millions of people can simultaneously watch a single event, such as the Olympics, or men walking on the moon.

While man dreams of traveling to the planets, unmanned probes have been blazing the trail for nearly three decades. The newest of these marvels, all launched from the Space Shuttle, are Magellan and Galileo, intended to send back detailed data for years on Venus and Jupiter, respectively, and the Hubble Space Telescope, designed to observe stars and galaxies as they existed 14 billion years ago, near the time scientists believe the Universe was formed.

These robot spacecraft have discovered some new worlds and wondrous things. Humans have caught the first views of the great storm systems and rings of Jupiter; the active volcanoes on its salt-covered moon, Io; the parched and cratered wasteland of Mercury; ancient river bottoms, raging winds and inactive volcano almost 80,000 feet high on Mars; sulphuric acid clouds, lightning, an active volcano, and hellish temperatures on Venus; the thousand rings and tantalizing moons of Saturn; a scalding 6,000-mile-deep ocean beneath the cloudtops of Uranus.

The spacecraft Magellan is released from the Orbiter Atlantis on day one of shuttle mission STS-30. After the Magellan deployment from Atlantis' payload bay, it began a 15 month long journey to the planet Venus where it will perform radar mapping operations.

From these flights, scientists are assembling a vast mosaic about the solar system and its intricate workings. A basic goal is to learn more about the Earth, fitting it into the cosmic puzzle that is the origin, the evolution and the structure of the Universe.

How we look from space.

Satellites monitor our weather.

*Pictured right
GALILEO, Far right
the HUBBLE.*

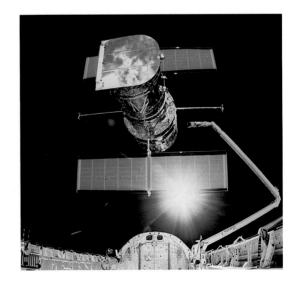

■ SPACE STATION FREEDOM

The centerpiece of America's space effort in the 1990's will be Space Station Freedom, an orbiting outpost that will install a permanent human presence out there and be a springboard for manned journeys to the moon and Mars. Starting in the middle of the decade, a series of about 20 Space Shuttle flights will be needed to haul up sections of the Space Station, and astronauts will assemble them in orbit. The station should be fully assembled by the end of the 20th century.

The project will be an international effort involving the United States, Japan, Canada and the 11-nation European Space Agency. Under an agreement, the U.S. will provide the largest portion - a crew module, a laboratory module, the truss to connect the various station elements, attached payload accommodation equipment, the power supply, other supporting resources and an unmanned polar orbiting science platform. Europe will provide a pressurized laboratory module, a man-tended free-flying platform and a polar orbiting platform. Japan's contribution will be another pressurized laboratory module, a facility to expose experiments directly to space and a logistics module. Canada will provide a mobile service center, a maintenance depot and a large robotic arm.

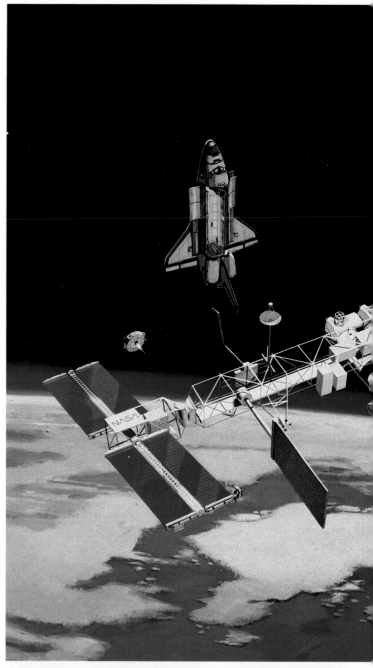

Orbiting 250 miles up, the station will provide living and working quarters for as many as eight people, with astronauts rotating back to Earth after four to six months. As a scientific base, the station will allow astronomers to study the stars and planets over long periods from the pollution-free environment of space.

The weightless world will permit the processing of new, pure medicines, metals and other products that can't be produced in Earth's gravity. And here, astronauts will assemble, service and repair satellites and send them out to explore space.

NASA wants to use Freedom as a launching point to send astronauts back to the Moon, to build a research base and to mine the resources there. Either the Moon base or the space station could be used as jumping off place for manned expeditions to Mars. The space agency is studying both options, and would like to mount such an expedition early in the 21st century, perhaps in cooperation with other nations.

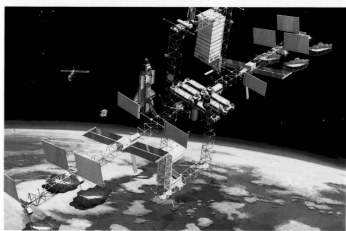

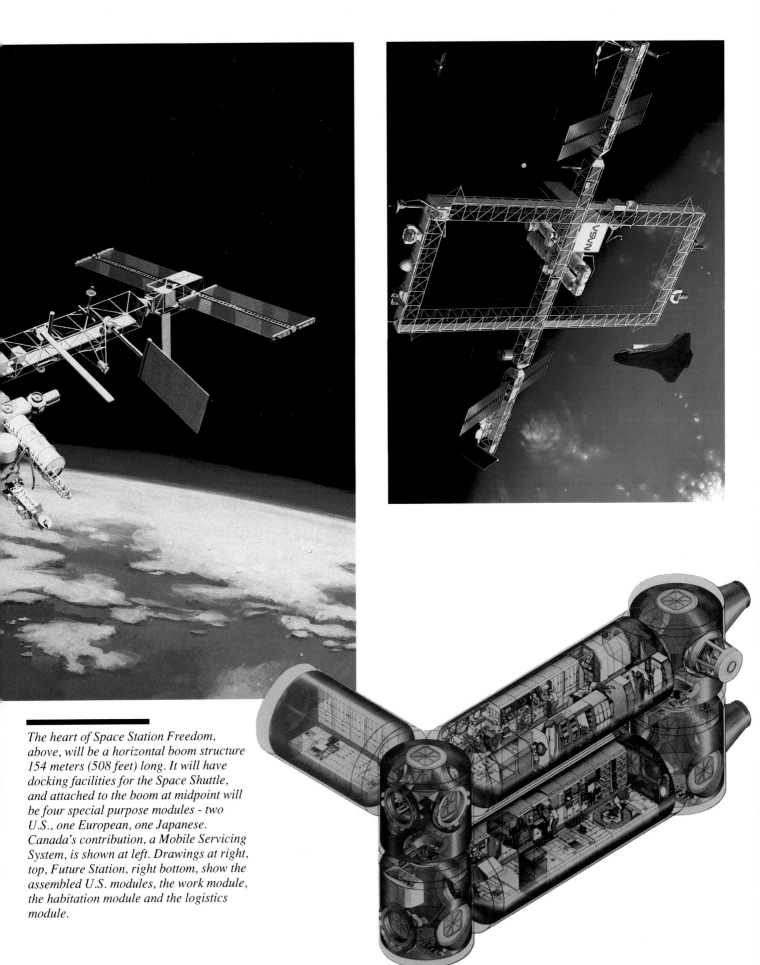

The heart of Space Station Freedom, above, will be a horizontal boom structure 154 meters (508 feet) long. It will have docking facilities for the Space Shuttle, and attached to the boom at midpoint will be four special purpose modules - two U.S., one European, one Japanese. Canada's contribution, a Mobile Servicing System, is shown at left. Drawings at right, top, Future Station, right bottom, show the assembled U.S. modules, the work module, the habitation module and the logistics module.

■ *RETURN TO THE MOON*

Only 12 humans, all Americans, have walked on the Moon. But none has visited there since Apollo 17 departed in 1972. Now, the National Aeronautics and Space Administration wants to return astronauts to the Moon early in the 21st century. Two plans are being considered. One would establish a permanent research base on the front side of the Moon - the side that always faces Earth. The other would be an occasionally man-tended astronomy base on the far side that is hidden from our view.

Astronaut construction crews would spend years building the permanent research base, with many of the building materials already on the Moon, as the Apollo astronauts discovered. It would be much like the bases now maintained on Antarctica by several countries.

Experience would be gained on all aspects of long duration space operations and the development of closed-loop support systems. A primary industrial goal of the base would be to mine the mineral resources there for use on Earth. The astronauts also would process lunar material to obtain Helium-3 in gaseous form, which could be used to power fusion reactors for electric power on Earth.

They could also process lunar soil to produce oxygen needed for use in their Moon Base and to propel spaceships to Mars. A base on the hidden far side of the Moon would be a delight for astronomers, who have long been frustrated by the fact that even with the most sophisticated satellites, their observations are hindered by the thickness of Earth's atmosphere and electronic noises generated by human devices. An observatory on the backside would have a clear, unimpeded view of the Universe.

Astronaut David R. Scott saluting United States flag.

■ WILDLIFE

The "wild side" of America's Spaceport is less known than the spectacular achievements for which the Kennedy Space Center is so famous, but it is also a treasured national asset.

Soaring along with the rockets here are Southern bald eagles, the national emblem. In fact, there are more endangered and threatened species at the Kennedy Space Center than at any other refuge in the continental United States. They are well cared-for by the dedicated workers of the Fish and Wildlife Service.

On the seven-mile Blackpoint Wildlife drive through the space center's Merritt Island National Wildlife Refuge, visitors can observe many of these animals, including alligators, otters, wild pigs, deer and raccoons. Activity is especially brisk in the early mornings and late afternoons between October and March. The mud flats and fish-filled waterways of the refuge offer a smorgasbord of food for birds such as the royal terns with their scarlet-colored beaks and black-feathered head tufts, the tall and picturesque egrets and the stately wood storks and great blue herons.

Among the inhabitants of the Spaceport are, clockwise from top right, Southern Bald Eagles, Manatee, Bobcat, Roseatte Spoonbill and Louisiana Heron, Brown Pelican, and Snowy Egrets. Opposite: A Great Blue Heron prepares for the oldest form of flight as man takes wing in the newest form.

■ COMMITMENT TO CAUSE

President George Bush has given NASA a strong mandate to pursue a strong, continuing space program well into the 21st century. It is the strongest presidential endorsement of space since President John F. Kennedy set a goal in 1961 of landing an American on the Moon and returning him safely to Earth before the end of the decade.

On July 20, 1989, the 20th anniversary of man's first landing on the Moon, Bush declared the United States should commit to a permanent presence in space. First, he said, the nation should develop Space Station Freedom and have it flying in the 1990's. Then, the president said, astronauts early in the 21st century should build a base on the Moon, and then embark on a "journey into tomorrow" - a manned expedition to Mars.

"Why the Moon? Why Mars?" Bush asked. "Because it's humanity's destiny to strive, to seek, to find. And because it is America's destiny to Lead."

In making his proposals, Bush became the first president to commit to these ambitious goals, and he set the stage for a full-scale debate on the future of the nation's space program.

Richard H. Truly, administrator of the National Aeronautics and Space Administration, said that while the moon and Mars "will be technically demanding and not without risk, they are well within our reach...These expeditions will stimulate new technologies and enhance our nation's long-term productivity. They will advance scientific knowledge and lead to discoveries about our solar system, Earth, and life itself."

Truly said the benefits of future mission to the Moon and Mars are difficult to quantify and include such intangibles as knowledge, success and pride. "Each time we go to the frontier and beyond," he said, "we bring back more than we hoped for. This time we have the chance to bring back more than we can imagine."

He said Space Station Freedom "is an essential step toward moving again beyond Earth orbit and into the solar system." Truly also said manned space exploration will stimulate science and engineering education. "I feel strongly that NASA has a special responsibility in education for a very special reason. Our programs - airplanes, spaceships, Moon, Mars and astronauts - can get to the kids."

Crew of the Shuttle Atlantis snapped this picture of a sunset with the planet Venus just above the horizon in the center of the photograph.

Printed in U.S.A. 12/92